SNOOPY

'it's a dog's life'...

by Charles M. Schulz

ℛℛ

Ravette London

This edition first published by
Ravette Limited 1987
Reprinted 1987

Printed and bound in Great Britain
for Ravette Limited,
3 Glenside Estate, Star Road, Partridge Green,
Horsham, Sussex RH13 8RA
by The Guernsey Press Company Limited,
Guernsey, Channel Islands.

ISBN 0 948456 79 5

'it's a dog's life'...

In his quest to write the 'great novel' Snoopy must suffer some destructive criticism and in spite of the artistic differences, he types on in search of inspiration. To find this, Snoopy need look no further than the humorous characters which surround him.

THIS IS YOUR NEW NOVEL, HUH?

I DON'T KNOW..

I GUESS I HAVE MIXED FEELINGS ABOUT IT...

2-5

© 1983 United Feature Syndicate, Inc.

I DON'T KNOW IF IT'S TERRIBLE OR AWFUL..

WHERE'S OUR PELICAN? THE GAME IS READY TO START! WHERE'S CHUCK AND THE PELICAN COSTUME?!

I TOLD HIM HE SHOULDN'T COME..I TOLD HIM IT WAS DEGRADING...

© 1983 United Feature Syndicate, Inc.

MARCIE!

THAT'S MY NAME

3-28

MARCIE!

YOU GOT IT RIGHT AGAIN

OUR PELICAN! HE'S HERE!

?

HA, MARCIE, YOU WERE WRONG! CHUCK DIDN'T LISTEN TO YOUR STUPID ADVICE! HE CAME ANYWAY!

TAKE THE HEAD OFF, CHUCK..I'M GONNA GIVE YOU A BIG KISS!

3-29

© 1983 United Feature Syndicate, Inc.

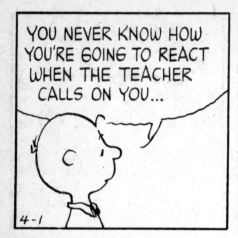

YOU NEVER KNOW HOW YOU'RE GOING TO REACT WHEN THE TEACHER CALLS ON YOU...

4-1

SOME PEOPLE TAKE IT VERY CALMLY...

OTHERS GET KIND OF STARTLED...

4-2

NO, I DISAGREE...YOUR ARGUMENTS ARE TOO ONE-SIDED!

BUT I'M SO MUCH BIGGER THAN THE REST OF YOU...

IT **IS** THE MIDDLE OF MAY, THOUGH, ISN'T IT?

OH, WELL...

© 1983 United Feature Syndicate, Inc,

5-23

THIS IS SO EMBARRASSING..

MAYBE, BUT I LIKE MY IDEA FOR A TITLE BETTER

I THINK YOU SHOULD TAKE MY SUGGESTION

© 1983 United Feature Syndicate, Inc. 5-24

It Was a Dark and Stormy Night II

COMB BREAK!

THAT WAS GOOD... I DIDN'T WAKE UP HIM NOR HIS LANDLADY

Dear Charles,
I have been thinking about you a lot.

Dear Chuck,
Life here at camp is great.

7-15

I think I like you, Charles.
love, Marcie

Don't listen to her, Chuck. She's not herself.

Dear Chuck,
Marcie got a letter from you today.

7-16

How come I didn't, Chuck? I wrote to you, too, you know.

How come you didn't write to me, Chuck?

~~Love,~~
Peppermint Patty

REMEMBER THIS...

7-25

BUILDINGS MAY CRUMBLE, BUT WISDOM IS ETERNAL

I HATE SAYINGS LIKE THAT

© 1983 United Feature Syndicate, Inc.

ALL THE BOYS AROUND HERE ARE SO DUMB!

7-26

I'D LIKE TO MEET SOMEONE I COULD REALLY ADMIRE

© 1983 United Feature Syndicate, Inc.

I'D LIKE TO MEET SOMEONE WHO IS HONEST, HAS A GOOD SENSE OF HUMOR, IS CUTE AND IS SENSITIVE...

JOE PERFECT!

RACTICING TBA'S

TBA'S?

"TO BE ANNOUNCED"

IF ANYTHING AROUND HERE IS TO BE ANNOUNCED, I'LL BE READY!

7-27

DOG FOOD! I'VE NEVER UNDERSTOOD HOW YOU CAN EAT THAT STUFF...

IT'S AN ACQUIRED TASTE

7-28

7-29

PLUNK!

THAT WAS A GREAT PUTT! HOW DID YOU EVER DO IT?

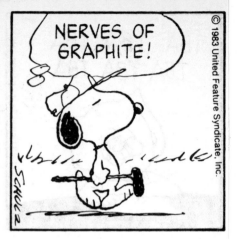

NERVES OF GRAPHITE!

© 1983 United Feature Syndicate, Inc.

YOU CAN'T REMEMBER HER NAME? TRY GOING THROUGH THE ALPHABET

7-30

SOMETIMES JUST HEARING A LETTER WILL JOG YOUR MEMORY...

© 1983 United Feature Syndicate, Inc.

SEE? ALMOST NEVER FAILS!

© 1983 United Feature Syndicate, Inc.

8-1

THE "RIPPLE EFFECT"

8-2

© 1983 United Feature Syndicate, Inc.

WHO ARE YOU?

I DON'T THINK I REALLY NEED THIS DOUGHNUT...

8-3

ON THE OTHER HAND, DOUGHNUTS ARE GOOD FOR YOU IF YOU HAVE SHINSPLINTS...

I CAN TALK MYSELF INTO ANYTHING!

8-4

IF YOU'RE LOOKING FOR ME, I'M OVER HERE

HERE'S THE WORLD FAMOUS SERGEANT-MAJOR OF THE FOREIGN LEGION LEADING HIS TROOPS ON A MISSION

AS THEY LEAVE CIVILIZATION, THEY APPROACH THE DESERT WITH ITS MILES AND MILES OF BURNING SAND...

© 1983 United Feature Syndicate, Inc.   8-5

WELL, MAYBE THREE OR FOUR FEET

I NEVER SEEM TO KNOW WHAT'S GOING ON...

8-6

RIGHT FROM THE VERY START MY LIFE HAS BEEN STRANGE

I THINK I KNOW WHAT HAPPENED..

© 1983 United Feature Syndicate, Inc.

I MUST HAVE MISSED ALL THE REHEARSALS

IT'S VERY STRANGE...

IT HAPPENS JUST BY LOOKING AT YOU

8-8

WHAT HAPPENS?

I CAN FEEL A CRITICISM COMING ON

© 1983 United Feature Syndicate, Inc.

I HEAR YOU'RE WRITING A DETECTIVE NOVEL

YOU SHOULD HAVE CHARACTERS IN IT WHO ARE LOOKING FOR SOMETHING VALUABLE

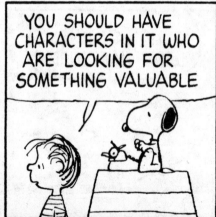

© 1983 United Feature Syndicate, Inc. 8-9

The Maltese Beagle

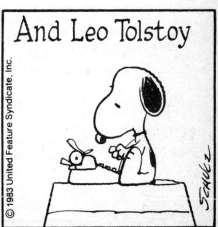

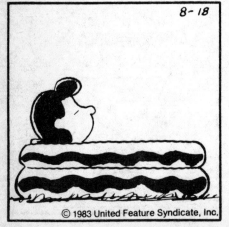

JOE HUNK!

HERE'S THE WORLD FAMOUS TENNIS PRO ON HIS WAY TO GIVE A LESSON...

DO YOUR STUDENTS PLAY BETTER AFTER TAKING LESSONS FROM YOU?

THAT'S NOT IMPORTANT

IF THEY TAKE LESSONS FROM ME, THEY DON'T GET ANY WORSE!

C'MON, TEAM, WE CAN WIN THIS GAME!

8-22

WE JUST HAVE TO PLAY TOGETHER... WE CAN DO IT IF WE ALL JUST PLAY TOGETHER!

WE CAN DO IT, TEAM! I KNOW WE CAN DO IT!

WE MUST BE LOSING AGAIN

HEY, GANG!

I HAVE A QUESTION FOR YOU...

8-23

HOW WOULD YOU ALL FEEL IF WE WERE TO MAKE THE PLAYOFFS?

OUT OF PLACE!

I WISH I HAD SAID SOMETHING TO THAT DUMB KID...

© 1983 United Feature Syndicate, Inc.

THE FRENCH HAVE A GOOD PHRASE, SIR... "ESPRIT DE L'ESCALIER"—"WIT OF THE STAIRWAY"

8-24

IT REFERS TO WHAT YOU WISH YOU HAD SAID BEFORE IT WAS TOO LATE

OH, YEAH? YOU AND WHO ELSE, DUMMY!?

ESPRIT DE L'ESCALIER, SIR...

ALL RIGHT, YOU TELL ME WHAT'S WRONG WITH DOGS, AND I'LL TELL YOU WHAT'S WRONG WITH BIRDS

YOU GO FIRST...

© 1983 United Feature Syndicate, Inc.

8-25

I THINK I SHOULD HAVE GONE FIRST..

HERE'S THE FIERCE VULTURE PERCHED HIGH IN A TREE WAITING FOR A VICTIM...

HEY, STUPID! THERE'S NO ONE AROUND TODAY... THEY'RE ALL AT THE SHOW, AND IT DOESN'T LET OUT UNTIL FOUR O'CLOCK!

© 1983 United Feature Syndicate, Inc. 8-26

I SUPPOSE A REAL VULTURE WOULD HAVE SOMETHING ELSE TO DO UNTIL FOUR O'CLOCK...

IN THE OLD DAYS, VULTURES USED TO SIT ON BRANCHES WAITING FOR VICTIMS...

© 1983 United Feature Syndicate, Inc.

8-27

IN THE OLD DAYS, THEY HAD STRONGER BRANCHES...

YOU'RE JUST JEALOUS BECAUSE I'VE ACHIEVED INNER PEACE!

© 1983 United Feature Syndicate, Inc.

I CAN FACE ANY PROBLEM THAT COMES ALONG

I HAVE SUCH INNER PEACE THAT EVEN IF MY SWEET BABBOO SAID HE DIDN'T LOVE ME, IT WOULDN'T MATTER..

8-31

I'M NOT YOUR SWEET BABBOO, AND THAT'S THE BEST NEWS I'VE EVER HEARD!!

I HATE EVERYTHING! I HATE THE WHOLE WORLD!

I THOUGHT YOU HAD INNER PEACE

I DO

9-1

© 1983 United Feature Syndicate, Inc.

BUT I STILL HAVE OUTER OBNOXIOUSNESS!

I HEARD YOU'VE BEEN TAKING GOLF LESSONS

WHAT DID THE PRO TELL YOU?

© 1983 United Feature Syndicate, Inc.   9-5

DID HE REMIND YOU TO KEEP YOUR EYE ON THE BALL?

HE SAID I SHOULD TEE IT UP SLOWER

SIR, WHAT ABOUT SCHOOL? AREN'T YOU GOING TO GET UP?

9-6

I'M AFRAID, MARCIE... LOOK OUT THE WINDOW... DO YOU SEE THEM?

© 1983 United Feature Syndicate, Inc.

SEE WHAT, SIR?

"D MINUSES," MARCIE! THEY'RE OUT THERE WAITING FOR ME!

AS SOON AS I GO OUT THE DOOR, I KNOW I'M GOING TO BE LEAPED ON BY A "D MINUS"!

NO, MA'AM, PATRICIA WON'T BE IN SCHOOL TODAY...

SHE'S AFRAID OF "D MINUSES"...SHE SAYS THEY'RE WAITING OUTSIDE TO LEAP ON HER...

9-7

NO, MA'AM, THEY DON'T FRIGHTEN ME...

I MUST ADMIT, HOWEVER, THAT I'VE BEEN STARTLED BY A FEW "C PLUSES"

© 1983 United Feature Syndicate, Inc.

SIR, YOU CAN'T STAY IN THE HOUSE FOREVER..YOU HAVE TO GO TO SCHOOL...

© 1983 United Feature Syndicate, Inc.

NO WAY! AS SOON AS I WALK INTO THAT SCHOOL, "D MINUSES" ARE GOING TO LEAP ALL OVER ME!

I KNEW YOU'D SAY THAT, SIR, SO I BROUGHT ALONG SOMETHING FOR YOU TO WEAR...

THAT'S NOT FUNNY, MARCIE!

9-8

DO THEY MISS ME AT SCHOOL, MARCIE?

ABSOLUTELY, SIR...IT'S A LOT QUIETER WITHOUT YOU THERE....

9-9

QUIETER?

WE MISS YOUR SNORING!

YOU KNOW WHAT I LIKE ABOUT SATURDAYS, MARCIE? THERE ARE NO "D MINUSES"!

YOU CAN GO OUTSIDE, AND KICK A FOOTBALL OR RUN AROUND, AND YOU WON'T GET LEAPED ON BY A "D MINUS"

WHAT ARE YOU GOING TO DO WHEN MONDAY COMES AGAIN?

9-10

I'LL BE BACK INSIDE WHERE THE "D MINUSES" CAN'T GET ME

YOU'RE WEIRD, SIR!

SEE? "ACE SLEEP DISORDERS CENTER."... THEY CAN TEST YOU, SIR, TO FIND OUT IF YOU HAVE NARCOLEPSY...

WELL, I'M SURE NOT GOING ALONE! IF SOMEBODY WENT WITH ME, IT MIGHT NOT BE SO BAD...

IF YOU CAN FIND SOMEBODY ELSE AROUND HERE WHO FALLS ASLEEP ALL THE TIME, THEN I'LL GO...

9-14

© 1983 United Feature Syndicate, Inc.

Z

HELLO, CHARLES? I'M CALLING TO TELL YOU ABOUT YOUR DOG

9-15

SNOOPY AND PEPPERMINT PATTY HAVE GONE TO A "SLEEP DISORDERS CENTER"... WHY? TO BE TESTED FOR "NARCOLEPSY"

THEY KEEP FALLING ASLEEP ALL THE TIME

© 1983 United Feature Syndicate, Inc.

IS THERE A CENTER FOR SOMEONE WHO FEELS HE NEVER KNOWS WHAT'S GOING ON?

HELLO, MA'AM... IS THIS THE "ACE SLEEP DISORDERS CENTER"?

A FRIEND OF OURS THINKS WE SHOULD BE TESTED FOR NARCOLEPSY... SHE THINKS WE FALL ASLEEP AT INAPPROPRIATE TIMES..

9-16

OBVIOUSLY, THE WHOLE IDEA IS RIDICULOUS...

Z Z Z

OH, I FORGOT... YOU'RE NOT HERE

WHERE WAS IT YOU WERE GOING? WILL YOU BE HOME FOR SUPPER?

9-17

OH, ONE MORE QUESTION...

WHY AM I TALKING TO YOU IF YOU'RE NOT HERE?

NO, MA'AM, WE'VE NEVER BEEN TO A "SLEEP DISORDERS CENTER" BEFORE

WELL, I GUESS I'M HERE BECAUSE I FALL ASLEEP IN SCHOOL ALL THE TIME

HIM?

© 1983 United Feature Syndicate, Inc.

I JUST DO WHAT I'M TOLD

9-19

9-20

YES, MA'AM.. THANK YOU...

THIS IS IT, SNOOPY...

IT IS?

© 1983 United Feature Syndicate, Inc.

SHE SAID, "GO DOWN THE HALL AND TURN TO THE RIGHT"

EVERY BAD THING THAT HAS EVER HAPPENED TO ME BEGAN WITH SOMEONE SAYING, "GO DOWN THE HALL AND TURN TO THE RIGHT"

YES, SIR, I THINK I KNOW WHY YOU PUT ALL THESE WIRES ON MY HEAD...

9-23

AFTER I FALL ASLEEP, YOU CAN TELL IF I'M NARCOLEPTIC IF MY "RAPID EYE MOVEMENT" BEGINS RIGHT AWAY...

INCIDENTALLY, HOW IS MY FRIEND, SNOOPY, DOING IN THE NEXT ROOM?

HERE'S THE WORLD WAR I FLYING ACE BEING TORTURED BY THE ENEMY...

SO HERE I AM LYING IN BED AT THE "SLEEP DISORDERS CENTER" WITH WIRES ALL OVER MY HEAD...

9-24

I WONDER IF THERE'S SOMETHING WRONG WITH ME.. I WONDER IF I'M GOING TO BE ALL RIGHT...

I WONDER WHAT SNOOPY IS THINKING...

WHEN DO WE EAT?

YES, MA'AM, I'M BACK! I WENT TO A "SLEEP DISORDERS CENTER," AND THEY SAID I'M OKAY...

THEY SAID I DON'T HAVE NARCOLEPSY, AND THE REASON I FALL ASLEEP IN CLASS IS I STAY UP TOO LATE AT NIGHT...

9-26

I DON'T THINK SHE CAN HEAR YOU, SIR

WHAT?

SHE'S ASLEEP!

YOU'RE BACK! HOW WERE THINGS AT THE "SLEEP DISORDERS CENTER"?

9-27

I SUPPOSE YOU LEARNED EVERYTHING FROM "A" TO "Z"! HA HA HA HA!!

GET IT? "A" TO "Z"! "Z" STANDS FOR SLEEPING... "A" TO "Z"... GET IT?

NO WONDER I SLEEP A LOT

THIS IS MY REPORT ON WHAT HAPPENED TO ME AT THE "SLEEP DISORDERS CENTER"

© 1983 United Feature Syndicate, Inc.

AFTER A BRIEF INTERVIEW, I WAS PLACED IN BED WHERE THEY ATTACHED WIRES TO MY HEAD...

NO, KID, THEY DIDN'T ATTACH ANY WIRES TO MY NOSE!

MAY I STRAIGHTEN HIM OUT NOW, MA'AM, OR WOULD YOU PREFER I WAIT UNTIL AFTER SCHOOL?

9-28   SCHULZ

© 1983 United Feature Syndicate, Inc.

NOPE, YOU WERE WRONG

THERE I WAS, SLEEPING PEACEFULLY...ALL OF A SUDDEN, I THOUGHT I HEARD A HUNDRED-VOICE CHOCOLATE CHIP COOKIE CHOIR CALLING ME...

I WONDER HOW I COULD HAVE BEEN WRONG ABOUT A THING LIKE THAT..

SCHULZ   9-29

YES, MA'AM..I WALKED ALL THE WAY TO SCHOOL IN THE RAIN...

9-30

MY HAIR HAS BEEN DRIPPING ON MY DESK, AND MY TEST PAPER IS SORT OF WET AND THE INK RAN A LITTLE...

ANYWAY, I'VE PUT MY TEST PAPER BETWEEN TWO BLOTTERS...

SO HERE YOU ARE, MA'AM..A TEST SANDWICH!

© 1983 United Feature Syndicate, Inc.

YOU'VE BEEN COLD AT NIGHT?

© 1983 United Feature Syndicate, Inc.

10-1

WELL, YOU COULD PUT BOOTIES ON YOUR FEETIES, OR YOU COULD LINE YOUR NEST WITH A WARM PIZZA!

HA HA HA HA!!

I WAS WONDERING IF YOU'D CARE TO DO MY HOMEWORK FOR ME...

IF YOU DID, YOU'D HAVE MY EVERLASTING GRATITUDE...

10-5

I DOUBT THAT

© 1983 United Feature Syndicate, Inc.

HOW ABOUT MY DAY-AND-A-HALF GRATITUDE?

BUGS ARE HOLDING THEIR WORLD SERIES IN MY SUPPER DISH?

© 1983 United Feature Syndicate, Inc.   10-6

I GUESS I'M JUST IN TIME FOR THE OPENING CEREMONIES...

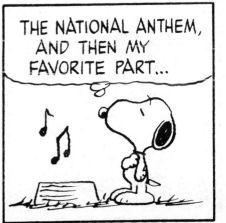

THE NATIONAL ANTHEM, AND THEN MY FAVORITE PART...

..WHEN THEY RELEASE ALL THE BALLOONS!

I HATE IT WHEN THESE BUGS HAVE THEIR WORLD SERIES IN MY SUPPER DISH

SOMETIMES THE GAMES CAN GET EXCITING, THOUGH

LIKE RIGHT NOW...

CRACK!

THAT'S THE FIRST TIME ANYONE'S HIT ONE OUT OF THE DISH!

10-7

WELL, THAT'S IT, I GUESS.. THE BUGS HAVE JUST FINISHED THEIR LAST WORLD SERIES GAME

NOW, MAYBE I CAN HAVE MY SUPPER DISH BACK...

OH, NO!

10-8

I FORGOT ABOUT THE FOOTBALL SEASON

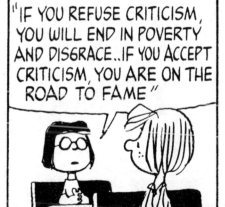

YOU LIKE HER, HUH? WELL, HOW ARE YOU GOING TO MEET HER?

CAN YOU DO A MATING DANCE?

10-12 © 1983 United Feature Syndicate, Inc.

MAYBE YOU SHOULD JUST CALL HER ON THE PHONE...

ONCE AGAIN, SIR, I QUOTE FROM THE "BOOK OF PROVERBS"

"WHOSO LOVETH INSTRUCTION LOVETH KNOWLEDGE"

© 1983 United Feature Syndicate, Inc.

YES, MA'AM, I LOVETH INSTRUCTION AND I LOVETH KNOWLEDGE...

I ALSO DON'T KNOW WHAT I'M THAYING!

10-13

AS LONG AS WE'RE JUST PRACTICING, I HAVE A SUGGESTION

MAYBE YOU SHOULD SHOOT AT THE OTHER GOAL FOR A WHILE...

12-27

© 1982 United Feature Syndicate, Inc.

WHEN ABRAHAM LINCOLN WAS AN ATTORNEY, HE WOULD ARRIVE AT HIS OFFICE AT NINE O'CLOCK

HE WOULD IMMEDIATELY STRETCH OUT ON THE COUCH, AND MUCH TO HIS PARTNER'S ANNOYANCE, BEGIN TO READ THE NEWSPAPERS OUT LOUD

I'LL HAVE TO REMEMBER THAT

© 1982 United Feature Syndicate, Inc.

THE SECRET TO BEING A GOOD ATTORNEY IS TO ANNOY YOUR PARTNER

12-28

SCHULZ

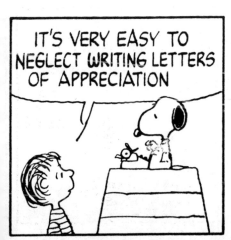

IS IT NEW YEAR'S ALREADY?

THIS YEAR I HAVE RESOLVED NOT TO BE SO SERIOUS..I'M GOING TO TRY TO LAUGH MORE

WHAT ARE YOU GOING TO LAUGH AT?

THINGS LIKE THIS!

KLUNK

IT'S GOING TO BE A LONG YEAR

PUT YOUR ICE SKATES ON, MARCIE..IT RAINED LAST NIGHT AND THE SIDEWALKS ARE ALL FROZEN...WE CAN SKATE TO SCHOOL!

THE KIDS IN HOLLAND ALWAYS SKATE TO SCHOOL

I DON'T BELIEVE THAT, SIR

2-6

PEGGY FLEMING SKATED TO SCHOOL EVERY DAY

I DON'T BELIEVE THAT, SIR

WE'LL GET TO SCHOOL A LOT FASTER THIS WAY..

I DON'T BELIEVE THAT EITHER, SIR!

© 1984 United Feature Syndicate, Inc.

YES, MA'AM...THE SIDEWALKS WERE SO ICY WE SKATED ALL THE WAY TO SCHOOL

DIDN'T YOU USED TO SKATE WHEN YOU WERE YOUNG, MA'AM?

2-7

DIDN'T THEY HAVE SKATES THEN?

THEY HAD WINTER, DIDN'T THEY?

© 1984 United Feature Syndicate, Inc.

YOU'RE GONNA BE PROUD OF ME, SIR...I'VE BEEN PRACTICING MY SKATING

THERE'S AN INDOOR ARENA ACROSS TOWN WITH A BIG ICE RINK AND A NICE COFFEE SHOP

2-8

WHAT HAPPENED TO YOUR ARM?

I FELL DOWN IN THE COFFEE SHOP!

I'M NOT GOING TO WORRY ABOUT VALENTINES THIS YEAR...

2-9

I NEVER GET ANY VALENTINES ANYWAY, SO WHY SHOULD I WORRY?

ON THE OTHER HAND, IF SOMEONE DID SEND ME ONE, I'D WANT TO BE THERE WHEN IT ARRIVED...

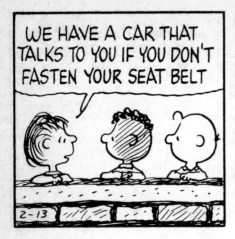

WE HAVE A CAR THAT TALKS TO YOU IF YOU DON'T FASTEN YOUR SEAT BELT

2-13

MY DAD HAS A CAMERA THAT TALKS TO YOU IF THE LIGHT ISN'T RIGHT

© 1984 United Feature Syndicate, Inc.

WE HAVE A MAILBOX THAT TALKS TO YOU IF YOU DON'T GET ANY VALENTINES

"SORRY, KID..THAT'S THE WAY IT GOES!"

RATS!

© 1984 United Feature Syndicate, Inc.

NOT GETTING ANY VALENTINES IS SAD

THERE'S ONLY ONE THING WORSE..

2-14

GETTING YOUR HEAD CAUGHT IN THE MAILBOX!

NINE? SIX?

ASPIRIN? MICE?

FIBERGLASS?

© 1984 United Feature Syndicate, Inc.

SORRY, MA'AM, I WAS LOOKING FOR SIMPLISTIC ANSWERS

2-17

YOU SURE LEAD AN EASY LIFE

IT'S ALWAYS INTERESTING TO SEE HOW THE OTHER HALF LIVES

2-18

MAKE THAT "ONE-EIGHTH"

© 1984 United Feature Syndicate, Inc.

I'VE LEARNED SOMETHING ABOUT WINTER CLOTHING...

IF YOUR SKI CAP IS TOO TIGHT, IT MAKES YOUR HAIR HURT...

2-20

THEN I OBSERVED SOMETHING ELSE...

BEAGLES SHOULD NEVER WEAR DOWN-FILLED JACKETS!

© 1984 United Feature Syndicate, Inc.

NO, MA'AM, I DON'T THINK WHAT HE SAID IN THE FIRST CHAPTER WAS GERMANE...

WHAT WAS IT, FRENCH?

HAHAHAHA!!

2-21

BONK!

© 1984 United Feature Syndicate, Inc.

THERE ARE A LOT OF PEOPLE AROUND WHO HAVE REAL PROBLEMS

MAYBE YOU SHOULD WRITE A BOOK THAT WOULD HELP PEOPLE

2-22

THINK OF THE WORST THING THAT CAN HAPPEN TO SOMEONE, AND THEN WRITE ABOUT IT...

What To Do When Your Beagle Leaves Home

AND THAT'S THE WAY I SEE IT! ABSOLUTELY, FOR SURE!

2-23

ACTUALLY, YOU HAVE YOUR FACTS MIXED UP, CHARLIE BROWN...

I DO? I GUESS MAYBE YOU'RE RIGHT

I HAVE VERY STRONG OPINIONS, BUT THEY DON'T LAST LONG!

LOOK, MARCIE, I GOT A FORTUNE COOKIE IN MY LUNCH...

IT SAYS, "YOU ARE GOING TO GET AN IMPORTANT LETTER"

2-24

IT WAS RIGHT... I GOT AN IMPORTANT LETTER THIS MORNING...

A "D MINUS"!

YOU SHOULD WRITE A NOVEL THAT IS REAL SCARY..

WRITE SOMETHING THAT WILL MAKE THEIR BLOOD CURL!

2-25

OR MAKE THEIR HAIR CURDLE!

WHAT DO THEY CALL THIS, MARCIE? A "YOUNG PEOPLE'S CONCERT"?

HOW DO I KNOW I'M GOING TO LIKE THIS KIND OF MUSIC?.

SHH...THE CONDUCTOR IS COMING OUT...WE'RE SUPPOSED TO APPLAUD...

WHY? HE HASN'T DONE ANYTHING YET

WHAT KIND OF A SHOW IS THIS, MARCIE? THERE AREN'T ANY PICTURES..WHAT DO WE LOOK AT?

THIS IS A CONCERT, SIR...JUST LISTEN TO THE MUSIC...

I DON'T BELIEVE THIS... AN AUDITORIUM FULL OF PEOPLE JUST SITTING HERE LISTENING TO MUSIC..

SOMEONE THOUGHT HE HAD A GOOD IDEA, BUT IT'LL NEVER GO...

YES, MA'AM, I ENJOYED THE CONCERT VERY MUCH.. I'M INTO CLASSICAL MUSIC

OF COURSE, SOME UNCULTURED TYPES TEND TO FALL ASLEEP, BUT WHAT CAN YOU EXPECT?

3-2

BLEAH!!

GIVE HER A "D MINUS," MA'AM...WHIP HER INTO SHAPE!

IT WAS A "YOUNG PEOPLE'S CONCERT," CHUCK...YOU KNOW, GET THE KIDS ACQUAINTED WITH GOOD MUSIC...

3-3

ANYWAY, AT FIRST I DIDN'T EVEN WANT TO GO, BUT AFTER I HEARD THE MUSIC, I THOUGHT IT WAS GREAT...

SO NOW WHAT HAPPENS? NOW WE HAVE TO WRITE A FIVE-HUNDRED WORD THEME ON THE CONCERT

BUT I GUESS THAT'S WHAT EDUCATION IS FOR, HUH, CHUCK? TO KEEP US FROM ENJOYING OURSELVES

 WHAT DO YOU CALL THAT?
 AEROBIC SLEEPING!

 THIS IS MY REPORT ON ACORNS, AND I BEGIN WITH A QUOTE FROM "SPOON RIVER ANTHOLOGY"
 "REMEMBER THE ACORN; IT DOES NOT DEVOUR OTHER ACORNS"
 I GUESS THAT MEANS YOU CAN GO HOME TONIGHT AND NOT WORRY ABOUT GETTING BITTEN BY AN ACORN! HA HA HA HA HA!!
 OKAY, WHERE WAS I?

YES, MA'AM ..UNDER HERE, I'M HERE!

3-16

3-17

© 1984 United Feature Syndicate, Inc.

3-23

YIPE!

WELL, MA'AM, MY MATH PAPER IS SOMEWHERE ALONG THIRD STREET, MY ENGLISH THEME WAS LAST SEEN ON SELBY AVENUE AND MY HISTORY PAPER IS NOW FLYING OVER HIGHLAND PARK...

TURN OUT THE LIGHTS, MA'AM, AND LET'S GO HOME!

© 1984 United Feature Syndicate, Inc.

Dear Snoopy, Guess what! I am studying medicine by correspondence.

© 1984 United Feature Syndicate, Inc.

It is quite fascinating.

I think I may become a specialist.

3-24

I plan to do hip joint replacements on coyotes.

I WAS JUST READING ABOUT WHEN CASEY STENGEL WAS A MANAGER

HE ONCE TIPPED HIS CAP TO AN UMPIRE AND A BIRD FLEW OUT!

THAT MUST HAVE BEEN FUNNY.. I WISH I HAD SEEN THAT...

4-2

HERE'S THE OUTFIELDER FOR THE DESERT TEAM WAITING FOR A FLY BALL..

© 1984 United Feature Syndicate, Inc.

4-3

WE'RE NUMBER ONE!

I'M GLAD YOU'RE NOT LIKE SOME BASEBALL MANAGERS, CHARLIE BROWN

I READ ABOUT ONE MANAGER WHO USED TO GET REAL MAD AT HIS PLAYERS...

4-4

IF A PLAYER DID SOMETHING DUMB, THE MANAGER WOULD PULL THE PLAYER'S CAP DOWN OVER HIS HEAD..

I SHOULDN'T HAVE MENTIONED IT...

SCHULZ

© 1984 United Feature Syndicate, Inc.

THIS WAS A GOOD SUGGESTION..IF A PLAYER MAKES A DUMB MISTAKE, I PULL HIS CAP DOWN OVER HIS HEAD...

Z

BONK!

© 1984 United Feature Syndicate, Inc.

4-5

I THINK I NEED A NIGHT LIGHT

SCHULZ